Golden Treasure

SCOTT, FORESMAN AND COMPANY • GLENVIEW, ILLINOIS
Dallas, Tex. • Oakland, N.J. • Palo Alto, Cal. • Tucker, Ga. • Brighton, England

Authors

Acknowledgments

Ira E. Aaron

A. Sterl Artley

Kenneth S. Goodman

William A. Jenkins

John C. Manning

Marion Monroe

Wilma J. Pyle

Helen M. Robinson

Andrew Schiller

Mildred Beatty Smith

Lorraine M. Sullivan

Samuel Weintraub

Joseph M. Wepman

Reader Consultants

Eleanor A. Dahlgren

Charles G. O'Brien

ISBN 0-673-10641-1   ISBN 0-673-10699-3

"Way Down Deep" from *Hello and Goodbye* by Mary Ann Hoberman. Copyright © 1959 by Mary Ann Hoberman. Published by Little, Brown and Company. Reprinted by permission of Russell & Volkening, Inc., as agents for the author.

From *Fish is Fish,* by Leo Lionni. Copyright © 1970 by Leo Lionni. Reprinted by permission of Pantheon Books, a Division of Random House, Inc. British Commonwealth rights courtesy of Abelard-Schuman Ltd.

Book jacket from *Jillions of Gerbils* by Arnold Dobrin, © 1973. Permission by Lothrop, Lee & Shepard Co.

Book jacket from *Maria's House,* illustrations copyright © 1974 by Frances Gruse Scott, reproduced by permission of Atheneum Publishers, New York.

Book jacket from *Dance, Dance, Amy-Chan!* Story and pictures by Lucy Hawkinson, © 1964 by Albert Whitman and Company.

Dick Brooks—pages 6–15
Ron Villani—pages 16–34
Rod Ruth—page 35
Phero Thomas—pages 52–67
Kinuko Craft—pages 68–79
George Armstrong—pages 80–92
Bob Gordon—pages 94 –115
Warren Linn—pages 116–117
Bob Masheris—pages 126–141
John Von Dorn—page 142
Ron Bradford—pages 144–149

Contents

Marvelous Machines

The Little Red Computer

by Ralph Steadman

"You!" said a deep booming voice. The little red computer looked up quickly.

"Me?" asked the little red computer.

"Yes, you," said the voice of the big robot teacher, pointing his finger right at the little red computer. "What does 2 plus 2 equal?"

A hush came over the mathematics classroom. The little red computer sat on the checkered floor and thought and thought. WHIRRR-RRR-RRR, SHHHHHHH, BLIP-BLOP went his circuits and switches. At last he was ready with his answer.

The little red computer began, "I do not know what 2 plus 2 equals, but—"

"Enough," boomed the robot teacher. "If you do not listen and pay attention, you will never learn. Now, go stand in the corner!"

"Oh, dear," thought the little red computer, "I am no good at mathematics at all." And he went sadly past the rows of other computers. They all looked very pleased with themselves, because they knew the answer was 4.

"You shall stand in the corner for the rest of the day," said the robot teacher, making angry whirling noises and flashing his lights on and off. At least nobody noticed how much the little computer was blushing, because the person who built him had painted him red.

So the little computer stood all day in the corner looking out the window at the flowers, the birds, the trees, and the sun. He thought a lot about these things and wondered at their differences and colors. Sometimes he was sent to the corner during night school. Even then he would look out of the window at the moon and stars. He would think about how beautiful and mysterious the night was. In fact, he spent so much time in the corner looking out the window that he felt he knew the moon and the stars by name.

Graduation day finally came. All the computers who passed their tests would go to work for engineers and scientists. They would work out difficult mathematical problems for these people.

The little red computer was the only one who did not pass his tests. He seemed to be of no use to anybody.

When school closed, he was cast into a field of grass, flowers, and trees. Bees buzzed and birds chirped, and both flew around him. The sun smiled down on him. The wind and the rain played little tunes on his square tin body. Even though he had not passed the tests, he felt much happier being with the things he understood.

9

Summer came and the grass and weeds grew up around and over him. But he was happy, because he could hear the shouts and laughter of children as they played nearby. Then fall came. One by one the leaves fell from the trees and collected in piles, and the air turned cool. The little red computer was still happy, because he could hear the movements of busy squirrels as they buried nuts for the winter. Then winter came. And the snow and ice covered everything with a cold white blanket. The little computer shivered. He felt very sad and lonely, and he started rusting at the corners.

Months passed. Finally it was spring! "Now," thought the little red computer, "I'll have company again."

The very next day workers came to the field with shovels, axes, bulldozers, and cranes. They put up a sign that said ROCKET SITE. Then they built a hut and filled it with boxes of expensive instruments and equipment.

Soon the workers started to clear the fields with their bulldozers and make holes with their shovels. Suddenly, the little red computer felt an axe strike his rusty side, and one of the workers shouted, "Look what I've found!"

All the workmen crowded around the computer. "Take it to the scientists," said the foreman. And the little red computer felt himself being lifted up and carried across the field. The workman came to the door of the hut and knocked.

"Come in," said a tired voice. The workman
opened the door. Three scientists were seated
around a table filled with papers and charts. All
three wore long white coats.

"What have you got there?" asked one of the
scientists.

"We found it in the field," said the workman.

"Hmmmm," said the other two scientists, and they
took the little computer and put him down in the
middle of the table.

"What it needs is a good cleaning," said the
workman. He took out a large white handkerchief
and started to rub away some of the rust and dirt.

That's when his hand hit the switch.

For a moment nothing happened. Then all at once the little red computer felt something inside him start to move. With a splutter and a BLIP-BLIP, he said, "I am sorry but I do not know what 2 plus 2 equals, but I do know many things about the world. I know about the moon and stars and outer space. I know what is beyond the big golden star in the northern sky. And I know that if you travel to the brightest star in the southern sky in the morning, you can be there in a single day and night. I know these things and many more, but I will never understand numbers," finished the little computer. He started to cry the only way a computer can. He shook his insides until they squeaked.

"Fantastic!" said one of the scientists. "There is only one computer programmed with this kind of information. It can solve all our problems. We shall leave for Venus right away, and we will take the little red computer with us!"

The little computer could not believe it! He was going to lead an expedition into space. He had never felt so proud and happy.

After a coat of fresh paint and several drops of oil, he was placed in the shining new silver rocket ship. On the day of the blast-off, the astronauts and scientists climbed aboard and all systems were GO.

9–8–7–6–5–4–3–2–1! For the first time in his life,
numbers really meant something to the little red
computer. These numbers meant the beginning of
an adventure into space.

The Secret of the Shed

by Antony Maitland

One hot summer afternoon Tom and Jane Robbins were working in their garden. To be quite truthful, they were tired of gardening. In a few days they would be starting school, and they did want something exciting to happen while there was still time.

Tom suddenly had an idea. "Let's go next door to see Mr. and Mrs. Marble," he said. "There are always lots of interesting things to do in their house."

Mr. Marble was an inventor, and his house was full of strange inventions. Many of these had never been finished, usually because he had forgotten why he was inventing them.

When the children arrived, Mr. Marble was too busy to see them, but Mrs. Marble gave them each a slice of cake and sent them out into the garden to explore.

An enormous black shed stood at the end of the garden. When Tom and Jane were in their own garden, they could hear strange howling noises coming from the shed. They had always wanted to know what was in it, but Mr. Marble never would tell them. He just smiled and pointed to the sign that said **SECRET.**

From *The Secret of the Shed* by Antony Maitland. Copyright © 1962 by Antony Maitland. Reprinted by permission of Hawthorn Books, Inc., and Penguin Books Ltd.

On this afternoon the children played as near the shed as they dared. There was nobody around, and all was quiet.

Then Jane noticed that the little side door was not quite shut. "Why don't we take a quick look inside?" she asked. "It couldn't do any harm."

Tom was a little older than Jane, and he knew he ought to say no. But he did want to see what was in the shed, so when they had made sure that no one could see them from the house, the children crept up to the door and looked in.

"Oh! Just look at that!" cried Tom.

"What is it?" Jane whispered.

There in front of them stood the secret of the black shed. It was a very strange machine, and it looked brand-new. Even in the dim light it sparkled and shone.

Tom and Jane crept inside the shed to walk around and admire the machine.

"It's called *Dabchick*," said Jane, reading out the name that was painted on the tail fin.

The door of the passenger cabin was open, so Tom and Jane climbed inside.

"It's just like being in the car," Tom said.

At that moment a terrible thing happened.

With a rumble, the big sliding doors at the front of the shed began to open. Someone was coming! Without waiting to see who it was, the children hid themselves behind the seats. In no time the shed was full of people who sounded very busy.

Tom and Jane hardly dared to breathe. They heard the door of the pilot's cabin slam shut. Then, with a great howling noise, the jet engines started up.

Above the noise came shouts of "Good luck, Mr. Marble!" and, with a jolt, the *Dabchick* began to move out of the shed.

Down the drive and out onto the main road went the little red machine. Soon it was whizzing along, passing everything—passing even the fastest sports cars. By this time Mr. Marble was so busy driving that Tom and Jane were able to creep out of their uncomfortable hiding place. When they looked through the round window into the pilot's cabin, they could just see the back of Mr. Marble's head bent over the controls.

They had been racing along for some time when the children saw a traffic jam ahead, but, instead of slowing down, the *Dabchick* rushed towards the cars.

"We're going to crash!" they cried.

But the crash never came. Mr. Marble pulled a lever, and the helicopter blades, which had been folded up, opened out and whirled into life. Only just in time, the *Dabchick* leaped into the air and skimmed away over the waiting traffic. The drivers down below were so surprised that they quite forgot to drive on when the long line started to move forward again.

It was all so exciting that the children forgot that they never should have been there at all.

"Let's tell Mr. Marble we're here," said Tom.

"Yes, let's," said Jane.

They opened the door and tumbled into the pilot's cabin. Mr. Marble got such a shock that the machine went quite out of control for a few moments.

At first Mr. Marble was very angry. "What are you doing here!" he cried.

Then Mr. Marble explained, "I'm testing the *Dabchick* for the first time, and I have to land at the airport when I've finished. They won't be at all pleased when they find I have children aboard."

Tom and Jane said how sorry they were, and the inventor forgave them and said they could stay in front with him if they behaved themselves.

When the children had settled into their seats, Mr. Marble sent a radio message to Mrs. Marble to let her know that the children were quite safe.

After a time, Jane shouted, "Look! There are Mommy and Daddy!" And, sure enough, far below they could see their home, with their parents and Mrs. Marble waving to them from the lawn.

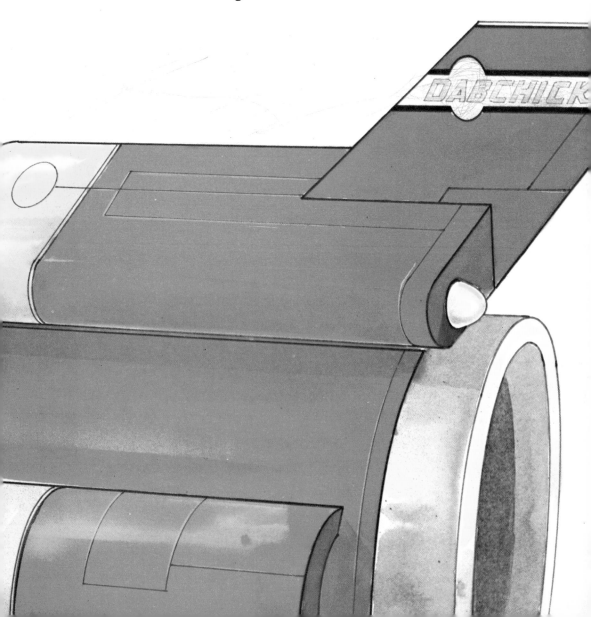

"We're going to the seacoast now," said Mr. Marble. He pressed a button marked Top Speed, and the red machine shot forward through the air.

Soon they were flying over the seacoast, where they could see the holiday crowds enjoying themselves on the beach. Then came the sea, all shining and bright in the sunlight.

"Now we come to the most important part of the test," said Mr. Marble when they were out of sight of land. Then, without telling the children what would happen, he pulled a blue lever.

The rotor blades stopped spinning and snapped into their folded position. With jets screaming now, the *Dabchick* plunged straight down towards the sea.

Tom and Jane shut their eyes tight as the waves rushed up to meet them. Then—SPLASH! They dived straight into the sea.

As soon as the swirling clouds of bubbles had cleared, the children were able to see that the *Dabchick* was moving down and down through the greeny-blue waters. The jets were now making a soft boiling sound. Great pink jellyfish drifted past the windows, and schools of fish swam by, their silver bodies flashing.

When it began to grow cold, Mr. Marble turned on a heater, and soon they were warm again.

Before long they came to the very bottom of the sea, and it was so dark that Mr. Marble had to switch on the headlights.

"Look!" Jane said, as an enormous octopus waved all its arms at them. The inventor shone the lights in the huge creature's eyes, and it was so frightened that it puffed out a cloud of ink.

They had been exploring the bottom of the sea for some time when Tom gave an excited shout. "Look over there!" he cried. "Isn't that a sunken ship?"

All three peered through the watery gloom and could just make out the shape of a great steamer.

Mr. Marble guided the *Dabchick* towards the wreck. "We must have a closer look at this," he said.

The little machine circled slowly round the rusty funnels and hovered over the deck. The ship must have been lying there for many years. Every part of it was covered with seaweed and barnacles. Crabs scuttled about, and little fishes swam in and out of the portholes.

"Good heavens! Just look at the time!" exclaimed Mr. Marble suddenly. "We must be off, or we'll be late at the airport."

Poor Mr. Marble was in such a hurry that he didn't notice the bits of ship's rigging that were trailing from the mast.

The *Dabchick* had just begun to nose its way to the surface when there was a scraping noise. Then a great jerk threw Mr. Marble and the children right out of their seats.

"What happened?" asked Jane as she picked herself up.

The *Dabchick* was still rising, but now it was going round in circles.

Mr. Marble looked very worried. He worked hard at the controls. "I'm afraid that one of the jets has stopped," he said at last.

Tom looked. "It's the one on this side. I can see a piece of rusty cable poking out of the front."

"Well, don't give up hope yet," said Mr. Marble, trying to sound cheerful. "I may be able to get it out when we reach the surface."

When the *Dabchick* had bobbed up into the open air, Mr. Marble was horrified to discover that the weather had changed for the worse. While they had been underwater, a storm had blown up, and now the first drops of rain were beginning to fall.

Mr. Marble looked anxiously at the dark sky and angry waves. "We must try to clear the jet and get away before the storm breaks," he said.

No sooner said than done. The inventor went into the cabin and opened the door. Then he climbed out onto the wing and started to crawl to the jet. But he was too heavy. The *Dabchick* started to tip and might have turned right over if Mr. Marble hadn't scrambled back just in time.

"It's no use!" he said sadly. "I'll have to send out an SOS on the radio. Then there's nothing we can do but stay here until we're rescued."

Mr. Marble started to work the radio. Tom

and Jane tried to think of a way out of their trouble. Suddenly Tom had an idea.

"Why don't you let me try?" he burst out. "I'm much smaller and lighter than you are. I could crawl right along the wing without tipping the *Dabchick* over."

By now the storm was nearly on them. Mr. Marble didn't like the idea of letting Tom do such a dangerous thing, but it looked like a matter of life and death.

"All right, Tom," he said at last. "You can try. But be very careful."

Mr. Marble opened the door of the cabin, and Tom carefully climbed out onto the wing. Jane and Mr. Marble watched anxiously as Tom inched his way towards the jet.

By now it was raining hard, and blue flashes of lightning split the sky. With each flash, Jane and Mr. Marble saw Tom moving slowly towards the cable.

Several times Tom was nearly swept away by big waves. Although his hands were getting stiff with cold, he managed to hold on, and the *Dabchick* didn't turn over. Soaked to the skin, Tom worked away at the piece of cable until at last he managed to pull it free.

"Well done!" cried Jane and Mr. Marble when Tom was safely back in the cabin. Mr. Marble gave Tom a large, warm coat to put on and told him what a very brave boy he had been.

Then, while Tom and Jane kept their fingers crossed, the inventor pressed the starter button. Both jets sputtered into life! "Three cheers for Tom!" Jane cried happily as they took off in a cloud of spray.

When the *Dabchick* came to the coast, the storm clouds rolled away, and the sun came out. The holiday crowds cheered the little machine as it zoomed over. They had seen it dive into the sea and thought it must have crashed.

Soon Jane saw the airport in the distance. The *Dabchick* approached the airport, and the children had a fine view of the great jet liners parked around the airport buildings.

They could also see a large crowd of people standing in front of the control tower. "Who can they be waiting for?" Tom asked.

"For us," said Mr. Marble as he made a perfect landing in a place that had been cleared for them.

The moment the motor stopped, people crowded around the machine, someone opened the door, and the children tumbled out. Cameras began to click in every direction as the crowd gathered around them to ask questions.

Tom began to tell about their adventures when Jane cried, "I see Mommy and Daddy!"

Mr. and Mrs. Robbins were smiling and waving. Mrs. Marble was standing beside them. Tom didn't finish his story. He and Jane pushed their way through the crowd to their parents. Mr. and Mrs. Robbins were so pleased to have their children back safe and sound that they quite forgot to scold them.

Before going home, they were all given a fine supper at the Airport Hotel. Mr. Marble made a long speech and thanked Tom for his brave deed. When he had finished, everyone clapped.

Then it was time to go home. The children

were so tired after their exciting day that they could hardly keep their eyes open.

Next morning at breakfast, Mr. Robbins showed the children his morning paper. There, on the very front page, was a big picture of Tom and Jane standing in front of the *Dabchick.* Below it was printed the full story of their adventure.

"It's a lucky thing you don't have to wait long to go back to school," he said, smiling. "You'll burst if you can't tell your friends soon!"

Talking It Over

1. What do you think the newspaper said about Tom's and Jane's adventure?

2. Why would Mr. Marble's machine be useful to own?

3. If you could invent a machine, what would it do?

Way Down Deep

Underneath the water
Way down deep
In sand and stones and seaweed
Starfish creep
Snails inch slowly
Oysters sleep
Underneath the water
Way down deep.

Mary Ann Hoberman

Bathtubs Are for Racing

This is Nanaimo, British Columbia, in Canada. It is a quiet fishing town on an island across the bay from the city of Vancouver. Nanaimo is also the Bathtub Capital of the World. Each year during July the annual Bathtub Race is held here. It is not a very old race, but it is becoming a very famous one. It is quite exciting, and people come from miles away to see bathtubs race across twenty-five miles of rough water to Vancouver.

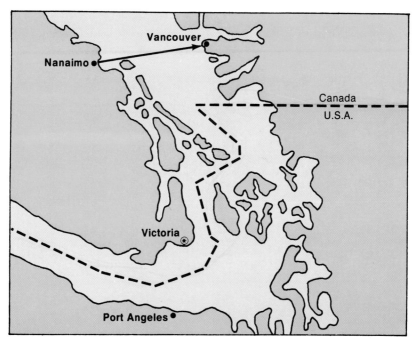

Approximate distance from Nanaimo to Vancouver—25 miles or 40.2 kilometers

There are many kinds of activities going on in Nanaimo the week before the race. Even the mayor of Nanaimo gets dressed up.

A king and queen are picked to reign over all the festivities.

There are not many rules for the race, but one rule is that you have to use a bathtub to race in.

This young man is getting ready for the race. He is wearing a rubber suit to keep warm.

Some men put the bathtub in the water.

Then the young man gets into the bathtub. The motor will be attached next.

It takes several men to put the motor on.

They lock the motor in place, and then the bathtub is ready for the race.

This motor is so big that it has to be attached to a platform at the back of the bathtub.

This man put wood all around his bathtub.

He uses a steam engine as a motor.

This man put one large ski on the front of his bathtub.

When all the bathtubs are in the water, they move to the starting line.

Everyone has a different kind of bathtub boat.
Which one of these bathtubs do you think is
the fastest?

The water is very choppy when two hundred bathtubs start the race.

Each bathtub has an escort boat. So there are
more than four hundred boats in the water.

The bathtubs go as fast as they can. Sometimes they go so fast they almost fly out of the water.

The bathtubs race across the bay to Vancouver.
Each racer wants to be the first one to see the
skyline of the city. People in Vancouver sit in their
boats to watch the end of the race. It takes about
three hours for the winner to get across the bay,
but some racers take all day.

As the bathtubs get close to the harbor of Vancouver, the racers can see the finish line. It won't be long until the winner gets the prize.

This is a picture of the first prize.

In the Present, In the Past

Louis Mofsie grew up in New York City. His mother was a Winnebago Indian. His father was a Hopi Indian who had come from a tiny Hopi village near the Painted Desert in Arizona.

Louis had never seen the desert. Neither had his sister. Then one summer their parents took them to visit their Hopi family in Arizona. This is how Louis told of things he learned about his people during that summer.

THE HOPI WAY

by Mary Elting

For three days and nights we traveled on the train—my father and mother, my sister and I. And then we rode miles over a dusty road in my uncle's pickup truck. What a long way it was!

As we rode along, my uncle hummed to himself. I asked him what he was humming.

"I am making a new song," he said. "A new song about you."

Then he sang a little of it and I knew it was a

happy song. But he sang in the Hopi language so I did not understand a word of it. He told us that the song was about children who came from far away to stay with their people for a while. Hopi people love to have sons and daughters come home.

We rode on and on until we came to the Painted Desert. People say the desert is "painted" because the earth is many colors there—purple, orange, yellow, green, and gray.

Beyond the desert lay the land where the Hopi people live. Hopis call this the Land of the Peaceful People, because the word Hopi means "People of Peace."

The road through the Hopi land grew even rougher and more lonely. But finally I saw a village of small brown houses made of stone. The houses were grouped together at the top of a steep rocky bluff. I could hardly tell where the houses ended and the brown rock began. I was glad to get there just at sunset, when the sky and the whole earth turned red and gold.

The next day my uncle took us to visit the members of our Hopi family. When the visiting ended my sister and I did not know who everyone was. But everyone knew us. And my uncle told me that they had all agreed it was time for me to receive a Hopi name of my own.

Of course, I had a name already. But Hopi children are often given several names. Later they can each pick the name they like best.

My grandmother had decided on a name for me. Long ago the name had belonged to a man in our family who followed all the special rules that Hopi people have worked out for living happily together. He was patient and generous and kind.

My grandmother wanted me to be like this

man, so she wanted me to have his name. When I received the name there would be a special ceremony.

On the morning of the ceremony my mother and sister went with me to my grandmother's house. When the door opened, I suddenly felt afraid. Around the room sat a row of women. Everyone sat perfectly still, without saying a word.

The women nodded toward a spot where my mother and sister and I were to sit. My grandmother placed a basin of water and a towel on the floor in the center of the room. Then she brought out an ear of corn and the leaves and roots of a yucca plant. She put the roots into the water and swished them around until bubbles formed. Then she motioned for me to come to the center of the room.

Gently my grandmother scooped up some of the bubbles and rubbed them into my hair. Then she took the ear of corn and stroked my head with it four times. Next, my mother did just as my grandmother had done. Then each of the women in the room did the same thing. This part of the ceremony seemed to take a very long time. But I tried to be patient just like the man whose name I was getting.

At last my grandmother wrapped a towel around my shoulders. Then she powdered my face with cornmeal and spoke my new name: Lomahongva!

"Lo-may-hong-vah." I said it slowly over and over. It had a splendid sound. In English it meant "Clouds-Standing-Straight-in-the-Sky."

Now the ceremony was almost over. There

was only one more thing to do. I had to make my greeting to the sun. So I took the ear of corn that had been used in the ceremony, ran outside and raised it high in the sunshine for a moment or two.

When I ran back into the house the women were all talking. They smiled at me and gave me presents. I could feel happiness rising up inside me, just as the yucca bubbles had risen up in the basin of water.

Later my uncle explained what my new name meant. "Clouds-Standing-Straight-in-the-Sky" were the great rain clouds that rise tall above the earth. These are the best clouds because rain helps living things grow in the desert. With such a name, a boy might bring happiness to his people some day.

He also told me more about the naming ceremony. The hair-washing meant that unpleasant thoughts were being washed away. The bubbles that rose like clouds carried a wish for rain.

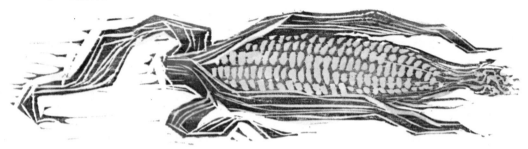

The corn had a special meaning too, because corn feeds people just as a Hopi mother feeds her family. The ear of corn at the naming ceremony meant that the corn was my second mother and would help me grow.

Soon I began to feel at home in our village. When boys and girls played games, I joined them. Sometimes we played in a large open square called a plaza.

One day I heard singing far away. I followed the sound and went across the plaza out toward the edge of the village. The song grew louder. I could hear many voices, but I could not see anyone at all. The voices were coming from under the earth!

Soon my uncle came along. When the singing stopped, we climbed down a ladder that went underground. We entered a shadowy room lined with blocks of stone. A little fire on the floor lighted the room. And I could see a group of men and boys standing about.

My uncle told me about this hidden room. It was called a *kiva.* A kiva was a sort of clubhouse, as well as a place for ceremonies. Every Hopi village had two or more kivas. A new kiva had just been finished in our village. Soon we would have a great celebration to honor it. People from other villages would come. There would be singing and dancing and feasting the whole day long.

Our quiet village grew more and more lively. All the people were busy, getting ready to honor the new kiva. They cooked and practiced the singing and dancing.

When the celebration began, the singers came first. Their voices filled the plaza with a tremendous sound.

Next came the dancers as bright as butterflies. The young men wore little capes and had sashes around their waists. Their white kilts, which were like short skirts, were bright with red, green, and black embroidery.

The young women each wore a *tablita,* which was a tall headdress. A tablita was carved from wood and was shaped like a row of mountain

peaks. It was painted with bright colors and decorated with downy feathers.

The dancers formed a long line from one end of the plaza to the other. Their feet moved in slow strong steps. While I listened to the singing, I could feel the pounding of the footsteps. It felt as if the earth had a beating heart.

When the singing stopped, it was time for the feasting and visiting to begin. All day long we danced and ate, going from house to house.

At sunset the celebration ended. Our village grew quiet again.

In the days after the celebration was over, my uncle continued to visit the old kiva. So did some of the other men. They were going there to weave cloth.

My uncle said that long ago men did the weaving for all the clothes that Hopi people wore. But now they wove cloth only for special things, such as the kilts that men wore at dances, or wedding costumes for women.

Often while one man worked at weaving, the others might sit and talk. Or they might make

pahos. A paho was made of string, feathers, and a painted wooden stick. A paho was supposed to carry a message to plants and animals that did not understand human language.

In the days when the Hopis had to hunt for all their meat, they first sent messages to the animals. Pahos told the rabbits or the deer that people needed them for food. Other pahos reminded the clouds to form in the sky. Duck feathers on a paho reminded the clouds to bring rain.

While some of the men were in the kiva, others worked in the fields that belonged to our village. The young corn plants were growing well. Almost every day some of the men went out to pull weeds. The boys often helped.

One day my uncle told me that the men would have a race when they came home from the fields. After that the boys and girls would have a race of their own.

We waited for the runners at the foot of the hill near the village. The last man who finished the race was hot, dusty, and smiling.

Now it was our turn. The boys would go first. But before we started, a woman handed each of us a stalk of corn and a piece of fruit.

The girls were not given anything. I wondered why, but I soon found out.

Off we went, up the hill. The boys started first. A moment or two later the girls came running after us. One girl caught up with us, and then another did. But they did not try to pass. Instead, they tried to snatch the corn and fruit away from us.

I dodged and ran on. "I'll win," I thought. But others ran faster. Nobody seemed to care who came in first and the winner did not boast. Some of the slow ones were praised, because they had run as fast as they possibly could.

A Hopi race is not always a contest for first place. Sometimes the runners only test their own strength and try to do their best. That is the Hopi way.

Our race had more meaning than any race I had been in before. It reminded boys and girls that they would not have an easy life. But the running was fun, so it also meant that hard work could be enjoyed.

We had a wonderful time visiting our Hopi people in Arizona. But when the summer was over it was time for us to leave for our other home in the city. Our relatives did not tell us good-bye. Hopi people never say good-bye. They want you to have the feeling that you will surely come back and that when you do, they will welcome you. That is the Hopi way.

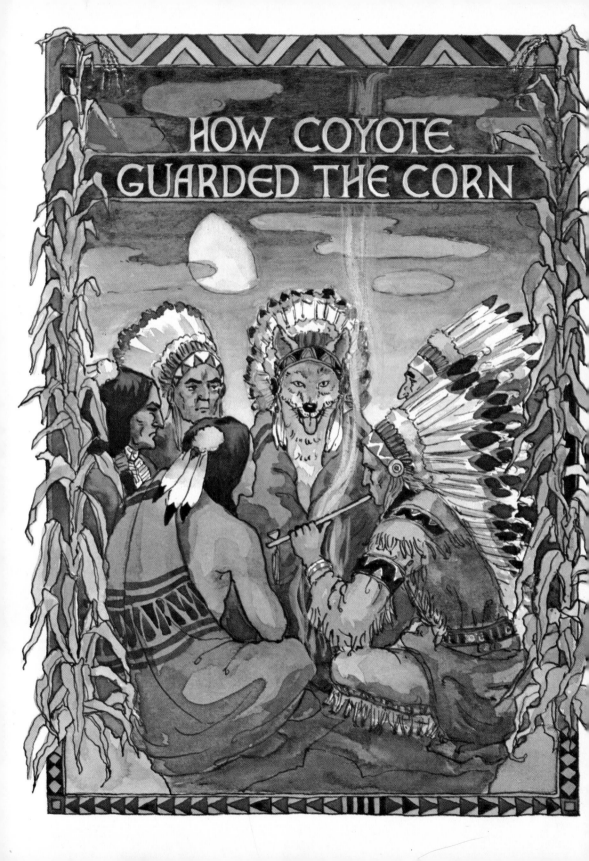

HOW COYOTE GUARDED THE CORN

The coyote is a character found in many American Indian legends that were first told long ago. In these legends, animals were bigger, stronger, and smarter than animals of today. The animals were as important as people, and they could speak the same language as human beings.

How Coyote Guarded the Corn
by Grace Jackson Penney

Long and long ago, there came a time when there was no rain in the land of the Cheyennes. Great clouds formed in the sky. The thunder grumbled and roared. But no rain fell.

Waterholes dried up, and streams stopped running. Corn and beans and squash and all the other food crops died under the hot sun. Berries and wild plums dried on the bushes without ripening. And the ground was so hard and dry that the women could scarcely dig up the roots that were needed for food.

Every day the hunters went farther from camp, but always they came back without meat. The prairie was so dry, that the buffalo had gone far away in search of water and food.

A group of great chiefs met to consider what was to be done. Then they decided to send an old man through the camp. He told all the people to bring the food they still had to a large storehouse.

From "How Coyote Guarded the Corn" by Grace Jackson Penney from *Tales of the Cheyennes.* Copyright 1953 by Grace Jackson Penney. Reprinted by permission of the publisher Houghton Mifflin Company and the author.

The men and women carried in the meat they still had, and they carried in all the corn that was left. They even brought corn that had been saved for planting. The squirrels brought in the nuts and acorns they had saved, and all the other animals gave the food they had.

The chiefs were to take care of the food and give it out equally. Everyone was to share and share alike, so that no one would starve while there was food in the camp.

The dry spell continued day after day, and the food supply grew smaller and smaller. At last there was only one small sack of corn left in the storehouse. It was the seed corn, and it was to be saved for planting. The chief who was chosen to guard the corn was O-kom, the coyote. He was honored and trusted.

O-kom went to the storehouse as soon as he could. He planned to guard the corn against anyone who might try to steal it. But as darkness came and the camp grew quiet, thoughts began to trouble his mind. The sack of corn was so small there in the empty storehouse. He walked all around it twice. Then he sat down and wrapped his bushy tail around his legs. Without knowing it, he was thinking out loud.

"That's a very small sack of corn," he said to himself. "A very, very small sack indeed. Divided among all the people it wouldn't last long or do much good."

Thinking made his ear itch, and he reached up with his hind leg to scratch it. That made his tail thump on the floor of the storehouse. The noise woke a little mouse who was dozing in the corner. The mouse was frightened, until he heard O-kom's voice.

"It's all very well for us to share and share alike, as long as there is enough to go around," said O-kom to himself. "But a little sack of corn like that wouldn't help anybody. It wouldn't even plant a very big field. And the crop might not grow if we did plant it." Mouse moved closer, so he could hear better.

"I'd better look at this thing in a sensible way," O-kom went on. "I must think of myself now. I could take this one last sack of corn and live on

it by myself until the rains come.''

Mouse was shocked that O-kom, an honored chief, could think such things. He couldn't believe it. But O-kom was still thinking out loud.

''Yes, that's what I'll do. I'll just put this sack of corn on my shoulder and slip out through the camp. By morning I can be so far away they will not be able to overtake me. But I'd better look out and see if anyone is awake in the camp.'' Coyote stuck his head out the door and looked all around. The camp was quiet. No one seemed to be awake.

Mouse thought quickly. There was no time to give an alarm. What could he do? Just as O-kom turned back from the door, Mouse darted into the open sack of corn and burrowed down to the very bottom.

O-kom put the sack on his shoulder and

quietly left the camp. He went so quietly that not
even a dog barked. It was very dark and very still.
But all the while Mouse was chewing away at the
bottom of the sack. Before Coyote had gone very
far from the camp, Mouse had chewed a hole
through the sack. He squeezed himself through
and ran back to camp to give the alarm.

"Wake up," he cried, running through the camp.
"Wake up! Chief O-kom has stolen our last sack of
corn. Right now he is running away with it!"

All the people sprang from their beds and started running after Coyote. As they ran, they made a terrific noise. O-kom heard them coming a long way off and ran faster. He was a fast runner, and he thought he would soon be so far away that he could hide until they gave up the chase. But he didn't know that the grains of corn were slipping out of the little hole Mouse had made in the sack. One by one they slipped out and fell to the ground, leaving a trail that was easy to follow.

Coyote was a very fast runner, but some of the people were fast runners too. They kept getting closer and closer, and Coyote ran faster and faster. He ran through some bushes and down a steep hill. He tried to lose the people, but they kept close after him.

He ran through the forest and out on the prairie, but all the people were still running after him. The fastest runners were in the lead. The slower ones were panting along behind, but they never gave up.

"I didn't know any of them could run so fast," O-kom said to himself. "I don't see how they follow the trail so easily. I'd better head for the mountains. I know I can climb faster than any of them. Then I can hide in the rocks."

So he raced into the hills and then into the mountains. Up high, when he thought he was safe, he stopped to get his breath and rest. But in a very little while he heard the people coming behind him, closer and closer. They sounded so angry that Coyote knew he'd better stay out of their hands.

He ran this way and that, looking for a place to hide, but the mountain peak was bare. There wasn't even a hole to hide in. He could hear the people coming closer and closer. They were moving in on all sides. He couldn't slip through and run away again. The people were so close now that he could see their angry faces. He had to do something. He gathered all of his strength together and gave a wild leap and went into the sky. He ran as hard as he could across the sky.

O-kom thought he was getting stronger as he ran, for the sack on his shoulder seemed lighter.

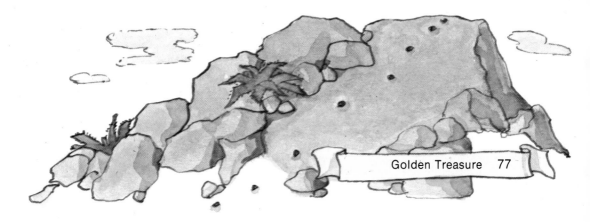

But all the time the corn was running out of the hole Mouse had made. More and more corn fell out as he ran. Soon there was a path of grains of corn all across the sky. At last O-kom reached the eastern edge of the sky. But the sack he had stolen was empty, so he got nothing for his dishonesty.

The people watched Coyote go across the sky, scattering the corn as he ran. Then they walked back to their camp, carefully picking up every grain of corn along the trail. They would save it for planting.

Not long after, Coyote came back to the camp. But the chiefs said he could no longer be a part of the tribe, and they took away his honors. Always after that O-kom, the coyote, was afraid to come into the camp circle. And always, when the people would see the pathway of stars across the sky that is called the Milky Way, they would tell the story of O-kom.

Talking It Over

1. Why did O-kom decide to steal the corn?

2. Why was it easy for the people to follow O-kom?

3. Legends were often used by the American Indians as a way to explain nature. What part of nature was explained in this legend?

TYEE'S TOTEM POLE

by Terry Shannon

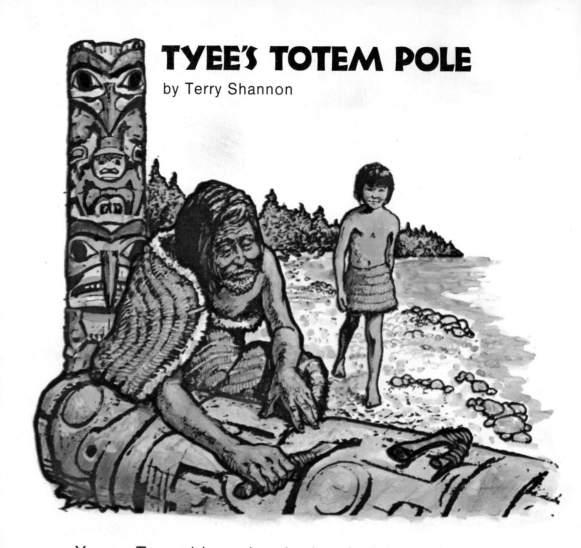

Young Tyee shivered as he hurried down the rocky beach of his village in Alaska. Spring was early that year in the land of the Haida Indians. He saw his uncle, Chief Whitefish, carving a totem pole. Tyee dreamed of the day he would spear a whale or catch the first salmon of the season. That would give him the right to carve his own totem pole with a special design.

From *Tyee's Totem Pole* by Terry Shannon. Copyright © 1955 by Albert Whitman & Company. Reprinted by permission of the publishers.

Soon Tyee's mother called, "Come, my son. It is
time for the noon meal. There is little food left,
but we will share what we have."

"Perhaps our fish brothers are angry with us, so
they stay away from our shore," Whitefish said.
"Always before we have had plenty."

Tyee joined the others around the wooden box of
fish stew. He said, "I would like to be the first to
catch a fine, big salmon. Some day I will catch
the biggest salmon there is. It will be so big it will
last until the next season," he boasted. "Then no
one will go hungry."

Whitefish looked at Tyee thoughtfully. Then he said, "My nephew, we shall make a canoe especially for you. You are old enough now to have your own. When it is finished, you may carve its bow."

Tyee and his uncle worked hard on the canoe for many days. Tyee sketched a raven and then carved it on the bow. Finally, the canoe was finished and ready for the water.

The next morning the villagers gathered in a group to watch Tyee launch his canoe. Tyee paddled close to the shore, then up the inlet to the mouth of the river. He stopped in the shelter of a large overhanging rock.

Tyee threw a hook attached to a long line over the side. "Perhaps I can catch a halibut or a cod," he thought. "That would help until the salmon come."

Almost at once his line jerked. He felt the pull of
a firmly hooked fish. As the line ran quickly
through his fingers Tyee braced himself. He
gripped his line hard to keep the end from
slipping out of his hand. The fish pulled hard.
Suddenly there was a mighty splash as the fish
leaped from the water in a struggle to free itself.

Tyee could hardly believe his eyes! There, at the
end of his line was the biggest salmon he had
ever seen!

Again and again the huge salmon leaped from the
water. The mighty splashes soaked Tyee from
head to foot. But the hook held fast. Tyee took a
great breath and pulled in more line. The fish was
worn out and lay exhausted on the water. With
one mighty haul, Tyee lifted the gleaming silver
fish into the canoe.

After he had rested, Tyee paddled closer to the
mouth of the river. The water sparkled with the
silver bodies of salmon! Tyee could see
thousands of them fighting their way upstream.
The salmon run had started!

Tyee would have liked to fill the canoe with
salmon but he knew this was forbidden until the
village had celebrated the Salmon Ceremony. So
he left the mouth of the river and swiftly paddled
back to the village. There he called to the
villagers and proudly announced the great news,
"The salmon run has started!"

Everyone came running. They all admired Tyee's wonderful fish. "It's a fine thing to catch the first salmon of the season," they said. "Tyee is greatly honored by our salmon brothers."

Then everyone got ready for the Salmon Ceremony. First the fish was cleaned with care. Part of it was returned to the water so that the

spirit of the fish could continue upstream. The rest was carefully roasted over a fire. Then Tyee called everyone together to have a small piece of the ceremonial fish.

When the ceremony was over the fishing gear was checked. It had to be in good condition for the next day when the salmon fishing would start.

Later that evening, Whitefish spoke to Tyee. "Now, my nephew," he said, "by catching the first salmon of the run, you have earned the right to throw the first harpoon tomorrow when the salmon fishing begins. And you have earned another right," Whitefish continued. "You may now carve your totem pole. The salmon symbol will be your own."

Tyee danced with delight. "I am going to carve my totem pole! At last I am going to carve my totem pole!"

Early the following morning everyone watched as
Tyee threw the first harpoon. He pulled up a
salmon. Then the rest went to work. It was hard
and tiring, but Tyee worked steadily beside
Whitefish the whole day.

When they returned to the village at nightfall, there were many baskets filled with salmon. Everyone was happy, especially Tyee. Food would be plentiful and soon he would pick a tree for his totem pole!

D-O-G Spells Fun

Ramona and Ribsy

by Beverly Cleary

One day after school Henry Huggins, who lived in
the next block, came over to play checkers with
Beezus. His dog, Ribsy, came with him because
Henry never went anywhere without Ribsy.

Beezus liked Henry because she knew he always
played fair, and the two often played checkers
together. So far Beezus had won forty-eight games,
and Henry had won forty-nine, not counting
the games Ramona had spoiled by tipping over
the checkerboard.

This afternoon Beezus and Henry knelt on either side
of the coffee table with the checkerboard between
them. Ribsy lay on the rug near Henry and warily
watched Ramona, who was wearing her rabbit ears
and riding her tricycle around the living room.

"Your move," said Henry to Beezus.

"I want to play," said Ramona, riding her tricycle
up to the coffee table and shaking her head to make
her ears flop. Ribsy got up and moved to a corner,
where he lay down with his nose on his paws to
watch Ramona.

"You're too little," said Beezus, as she moved a checker. "Besides, only two can play checkers."

"We could play tiddlywinks," said Ramona. "I know how to play tiddlywinks."

Beezus did not answer. Her mind was on the game as she watched Henry's move very carefully.

"I said we could play tiddlywinks," yelled Ramona.

Beezus looked up from the checkerboard. "Ramona, you stop bothering us," she said in her severest voice.

Ramona scowled and pedaled backwards away from the coffee table while Beezus returned to her game and studied the board. She had to be careful because Henry had already captured half of her checkers. "Let's see," she thought. "I could move from here to there—no, that wouldn't work because then he could—but if I move from there to there—yes, that was it!" Beezus lifted her hand to pick up the checker.

At that instant Ramona pedaled as fast as she could toward the coffee table. Crash! The front wheel of Ramona's tricycle rammed into the table. Checkers bounced into the air and showered over the table, falling to the floor and rolling across the rug.

"There!" said Ramona, and calmly pedaled away.

"Hey!" protested Henry.

"Mother!" Beezus called. "Ramona's bothering us!"

When mother heard Beezus call, she came out of the next room. "Ramona, you know you're not supposed to bother Henry and Beezus when they're playing checkers. Now go to your room and stay there until you are able to behave yourself."

"No," said Ramona. "I don't have anybody to play with me, and I want Beezus and Henry to play with me."

"You heard me," said mother, as she lifted Ramona off the tricycle.

"I'll bet she has a tantrum," thought Beezus, as she picked up the checkers.

"No!" screamed Ramona.

"Ramona," said mother in a warning voice. "I'm going to count to ten."

Ramona threw herself on the floor and kicked and screamed.

"One—two—," began mother.

Ramona went on kicking and screaming until mother counted to seven. Then she lay still on the floor, watching to see if mother really meant what she said.

"Eight—nine—," said mother.

Ramona got to her feet, ran into the bedroom, and slammed the door. Mother returned to the kitchen, and Beezus and Henry started a new game as if nothing had happened. Tantrums were not unusual in the Quimby household. Even Henry knew that.

In a few minutes Beezus heard Ramona open the bedroom door. "Now can I come out?" she called.

"Can you stop bothering Beezus and Henry?" mother asked from the kitchen.

"No," said Ramona, and shut the door.

Not more than one minute later Ramona opened the door again and came into the living room. "I can stop bothering," she said, with a sulky look on her face, and Beezus could see she was still cross because she had been punished.

"That's good," called mother. "Come here, and I'll give you a cookie."

Seeing Ramona go into the kitchen, Ribsy sat up, scratched, and trotted after her. Although Ribsy did not trust Ramona, he was always interested in what went on in a kitchen.

"I hope she stays in the kitchen," thought Beezus, as she picked up a checker and skipped from here to there to there and captured two of Henry's men. The game became so exciting that Beezus almost forgot about Ramona. At the same time she was vaguely aware of scuffling sounds in the hall. Then she heard the jingle of Ribsy's license tags and the click of his claws on the hardwood floor. Ribsy gave a short bark. Then the bathroom door slammed.

"I wonder what Ramona is doing," thought Beezus, as she captured another checker, but she did not much care so long as Ramona did not interrupt the game.

"Let me in!" screamed Ramona from the hall. "Let me in the bathroom."

"Ramona, who are you talking to?" asked mother, as she went into the hall.

"Ribsy," said Ramona, and beat on the door with her fists.

Ribsy began to bark. From behind the bathroom door, his barks made a hollow, echoing sound. Puzzled, Henry looked at Beezus. Ribsy in the bathroom? Henry decided he had better investigate. Reluctantly, Beezus left the game and followed him into the hall.

"Open the door and let him out," said mother.

"I can't," shouted Ramona angrily, above Ribsy's barks. "The bad old dog went and locked the door."

"Oh, stop pretending." Beezus was exasperated with Ramona for interrupting the game a second time. It was too bad that a girl couldn't have a friend over for a game of checkers without her little sister spoiling all her fun.

"I'm not pretending," screamed Ramona, clinging to the doorknob while Ribsy barked and scratched at the other side of the door.

"Ramona!" Mother's voice was stern. "Let that dog out."

"I can't," cried Ramona, rattling the bathroom door. "The bad old dog locked me out."

"Nonsense. Dogs can't lock doors," scolded mother. "Now open that door and let him out."

Ramona began to sob, and Ribsy barked louder. Ramona gave the door a good hard kick.

"Oh, for Pete's sake," muttered Henry.

"Ramona, I am very cross with you," said mother. She pried Ramona's fingers loose and started to open the door. The knob would not turn. "That's strange," she remarked, and rattled the door herself. Then she hit the door with her fist to see if it might be stuck. The door did not budge. There was no doubt about it. The bathroom door was locked.

"But how could it be locked?" Henry asked.

"I told you Ribsy locked it," Ramona shouted.

"Don't be silly," said Beezus impatiently.

"Now how on earth—," began mother in a puzzled voice, and then she interrupted herself. "Do you suppose when Ribsy was pawing at the door, he bumped against the button in the center of the knob and really did lock the door? Of course! That's exactly what must have happened."

"A dog that locked the bathroom door! That Ribsy," thought Beezus. "He's always getting into trouble, and now he's locked the Quimbys out of their bathroom."

"I told you he locked the door," Ramona said.

"Yes, but what was my dog doing in the bathroom in the first place?" Henry demanded.

"I put him there," said Ramona.

"Ramona Quimby!" Even mother sounded exasperated. "Sometimes I don't know what gets into you. You know dogs don't belong in the bathroom. Now go to your room and stay there until I tell you to come out."

"Yes, but—," Ramona began.

"I don't want to have to speak to you again." It was unusual for mother to be as stern as this.

Still crying, Ramona went to her room, which was next to the bathroom. Since mother had not told her to close the door, Ramona stood just inside it and waited to see what would happen next.

"Where is the key?" Beezus asked.

"I don't know," answered mother. "I don't remember that we ever had a key."

"But there's a keyhole," said Beezus. "There must be a key."

"Ribsy, be quiet," ordered Henry. "We'll get you out." But Ribsy only barked harder, and his barks echoed and re-echoed around the small room.

"No one gave us a key to the bathroom when we rented the house," explained mother. "And when Ramona first learned to walk, we fastened the button down with Scotch tape so she couldn't lock herself in."

"You did?" Ramona, fascinated with this bit of infor- mation about herself, stopped crying and leaned

out into the hall. "How big was I then?" No one
bothered to answer her.

"We've got to get Ribsy out of the bathroom,"
said Beezus.

"Yes," agreed mother. "But how?"

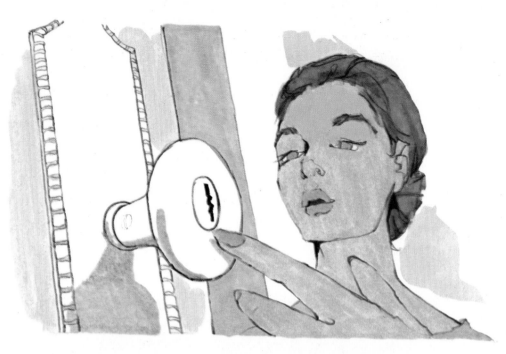

"If you have a ladder, I'll climb in the bathroom window and unlock the door," Henry offered.

"The window is locked too," said mother, bending over to examine the knob of the door.

"Maybe we could call the fire department," Henry suggested. "They're always rescuing cats and things."

"They couldn't do anything with the bathroom window locked," Beezus pointed out.

"I guess that's right." Henry sounded disappointed. It would have been exciting to have the fire department rescue Ribsy.

"Well, I just can't see any way to take the knob off," said mother. "There aren't any screws on this side of the door."

"We've got to get him out some way," said Henry. "We can't leave him in there. He'll get hungry."

Beezus did not think this remark of Henry's was very thoughtful. Of course Ribsy would get hungry if he stayed in the bathroom long enough, but on the other hand they would need their bathroom, and it was Henry's dog who had locked them out.

Then Beezus made a suggestion. "Maybe if we pushed some glue under the door so Ribsy would get his paws in it and then called to him so he would scratch at the door, maybe his paws would stick to the button in the knob, and he could unlock it himself." Beezus thought her idea was a good one until she saw the disgusted look on Henry's face. "I just thought it might work," she said apologetically.

"Mother—," began Ramona, leaning out into the hall.

Mother paid no attention to her. "I just don't see what we can do—"

"*Mother*," said Ramona urgently. This time she stepped into the hall.

"Unless we get a ladder (go back to your room, Ramona) and break the window so we can unlock it," mother continued, speaking with one sentence inside another, the way grown-ups so often did with Ramona around.

"But *mother*," insisted Ramona even more urgently. "I have to—"

"Oh, dear, I might have known," sighed mother. "Well, come on. I'll take you next door."

"Leave it to Ramona," thought Beezus, embarrassed to have Ramona behave this way in front of Henry.

"Don't worry, Ribsy," said Henry. "We'll get you out somehow." He turned to Beezus and said gloomily, "If we don't get him out by dinner time, maybe we could cut some meat up in real little pieces and shove it under the door to him. I don't see how we could get a drink of water to him though."

"We have to get him out before then," said Beezus. "Father wouldn't like it if he came home and found Ribsy had locked him out of the bathroom."

"Ribsy couldn't have locked the door if Ramona hadn't put him in the bathroom in the first place," Henry pointed out. "What a dumb thing to do!"

Beezus had nothing to say to this. What could she say when it really had been Ramona's fault?

Mother and Ramona soon returned. "I think we'll get Ribsy out now," said mother cheerfully. "The lady next door says her little grandson locks himself in the bathroom every time he comes to visit her, and she always unlocks the door with a nail file. She told me how to do it." Mother found a nail file, which she inserted in the keyhole. She wiggled it around, the doorknob clicked, and mother opened the door. It was as easy as that!

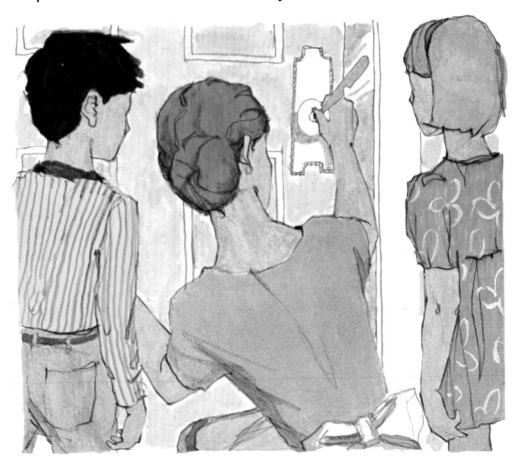

With a joyous bark, Ribsy bounded out and jumped up on Henry. "Good old Ribsy," said Henry. "Did you think we were going to leave you in there?" Ribsy wriggled and wagged his tail happily because he was free at last.

"Now maybe he'll be a good dog," said Ramona sulkily.

"He is a good dog, aren't you, Ribsy?" Henry patted him.

"He is *not* a good dog," contradicted Ramona. "He took my cookie away from me and gobbled it right up."

"Oh," said Henry uncomfortably. "I didn't know he ate your cookie."

"Well, he did," said Ramona, "and I made him go in the bathroom until he could be a good dog."

From the way Henry looked at Ramona, Beezus could tell he didn't think much of her reason for shutting Ribsy in the bathroom.

"Oh, Ramona." Mother looked amused and exasperated at the same time. "Just because you were sent to your room is no reason for you to try to punish Henry's dog."

"It is too," said Ramona defiantly. "He was bad."

"Well, I guess I better be going," said Henry. "Come on, Ribsy."

"Don't go, Henry," begged Beezus. "Maybe we could go out on the porch or someplace and play a game."

"Some other time maybe," answered Henry. "I've got things to do."

"All right," agreed Beezus reluctantly. Henry probably knew they wouldn't be safe from Ramona anywhere, the way she was behaving today.

When Henry had gone, Ramona gave a hop to make her rabbit ears flop. *"Now* we can play tiddlywinks!" she announced, as if she had been waiting for this moment all afternoon.

"No, we can't," snapped Beezus, who couldn't remember when she had been so annoyed with Ramona.

"Yes, we can," said Ramona. "Henry's gone now."

"We can't because I won't play. So there!" Beezus answered. It wasn't as though Henry came over every day to play checkers. He came only once in a while, and then they couldn't play because Ramona was so awful.

Just then the telephone rang, and Mother answered it. "Oh, hello, Beatrice," Beezus heard her say. "I was hoping you'd call."

"Tiddlywinks, tiddlywinks, I want to play tiddlywinks," chanted Ramona, shaking her head back and forth.

"Not after the way you spoiled our checker game,"
said Beezus. "I wouldn't play tiddlywinks with you
for a million dollars."

"Yes!" shouted Ramona.

"Children!" Mother put her hand over the mouthpiece
of the telephone. "I'm trying to talk to your
Aunt Beatrice."

For a moment Beezus forgot her quarrel with Ramona. "Is she coming over today?" she asked eagerly.

"Not today." Mother smiled at Beezus. "But I'll tell her you wish she'd come."

"Tell her she hasn't been here for two whole weeks," said Beezus.

"Tiddlywinks, tiddlywinks," chanted Ramona, more quietly this time. "We're going to play tiddlywinks."

"We are not!" whispered Beezus furiously. And as she looked at Ramona, a terrible thought came to her. Right that very instant she was so exasperated with Ramona that she did not like her at all. Not one little bit. Crashing her tricycle into the checker-board, throwing a tantrum, and shoving a dog into the bathroom—how could one four-year-old be such a pest all in one afternoon? And Ramona wasn't one bit sorry about it either. She was glad she had driven Henry home with her naughtiness.

"Just look at her," thought Beezus, "cookie crumbs sticking to the front of her overalls, her hands and face dirty, and those silly paper ears. She's just awful, that's what she is, perfectly awful—and she looks so cheerful. To look at her, you wouldn't know she'd done a thing. She's spoiled my whole afternoon, and she's happy. She even thinks she'll get me to play tiddlywinks with her. Well, I won't. I won't because I don't like her *one little bit!*"

To get away from Ramona, Beezus stalked into the living room and threw herself into her father's big chair. "Not one little bit," she thought fiercely.

But as Beezus sat listening to her mother chatting and laughing over the telephone, she began to feel uncomfortable. She ought to like Ramona. Sisters always liked each other. They were supposed to— like mother and Aunt Beatrice. "But that was different," Beezus thought quickly. Aunt Beatrice wasn't like Ramona. She was—well, she was Aunt Beatrice, loving and understanding and full of fun. Ramona was noisy and grubby and exasperating.

"I feel so mixed up," thought Beezus. "Sometimes I don't like Ramona at all, and I'm supposed to like her because she's my sister, and—oh, dear, even if she's little, can't she ever be more like other people's sisters?"

Talking It Over

1. Name three ideas in the story for unlocking the door.

2. Have you ever felt the same way as one of the characters in the story? Tell about it.

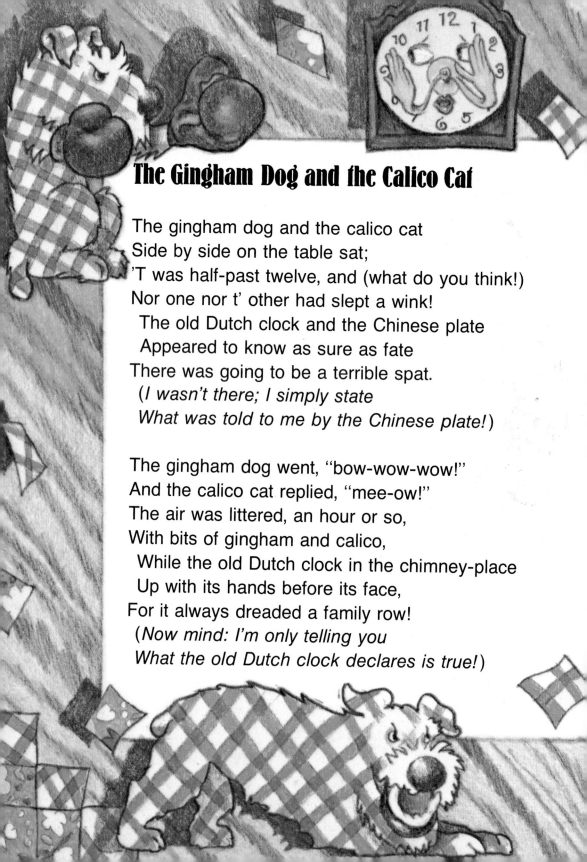

The Gingham Dog and the Calico Cat

The gingham dog and the calico cat
Side by side on the table sat;
'T was half-past twelve, and (what do you think!)
Nor one nor t' other had slept a wink!
  The old Dutch clock and the Chinese plate
  Appeared to know as sure as fate
There was going to be a terrible spat.
  (*I wasn't there; I simply state*
  What was told to me by the Chinese plate!)

The gingham dog went, "bow-wow-wow!"
And the calico cat replied, "mee-ow!"
The air was littered, an hour or so,
With bits of gingham and calico,
  While the old Dutch clock in the chimney-place
  Up with its hands before its face,
For it always dreaded a family row!
  (*Now mind: I'm only telling you*
  What the old Dutch clock declares is true!)

The Chinese plate looked very blue,
And wailed, "Oh, dear! what shall we do!"
But the gingham dog and the calico cat
Wallowed this way and tumbled that,
  Employing every tooth and claw
  In the awfullest way you ever saw—
And, oh! how the gingham and calico flew!
  (*Don't fancy I exaggerate—*
  I got my news from the Chinese plate!)

Next morning, where the two had sat
They found no trace of dog or cat;
And some folks think unto this day
That burglars stole that pair away!
  But the truth about the cat and pup
  Is this: they ate each other up!
Now what do you really think of that!
  (*The old Dutch clock it told me so,*
  And that is how I came to know.)

Eugene Field

117

A NEW PUPPY

A dog makes a wonderful pet. Before you get one, there are some things you should know.

A puppy should be about eight weeks old when you take him away from his mother. When you see a puppy that you like, make sure he's a healthy one. A healthy puppy has a shiny coat and bright eyes.

A new puppy is like a new baby. People and places might scare him, so you must be very gentle with him. Don't play too hard with him, and when he gets tired, let him take a nap.

You can make a bed for the puppy out of a box. Put some old blankets or towels in the box. Make sure the bed is in a quiet place so the puppy can sleep. Don't put the bed near a radiator or on a cement floor. It shouldn't be too hot or too cold.

The puppy should have one bowl for water and one for food. Put fresh cool water in one bowl every day. Ask a veterinarian what to feed the puppy. Put the food in the other bowl. If the puppy doesn't eat all the food in the bowl, throw it away. It might spoil and make him sick.

A new puppy loves to chew on everything. He is getting new teeth, and chewing makes him feel better. Give him a hard ball to chew on. Or you can buy a toy bone for him, but don't give him a real bone. The puppy might get splinters from it and hurt himself.

You should start to housebreak your puppy
as soon as you bring him home. Take him outside
right after he eats and after he wakes up from a
nap. When he gets older, he won't have to go
outside so often. It's also fun to take him outside
just to play.

Is It Realistic or Informational?

There are many different kinds of selections in this book. Some of the selections that you have read were about real things that actually happened. Some of the selections that you have read were about things that were not true and did not actually happen.

Look at the contents on pages 3 and 4. Think about the selections you have read and remember what each selection was about.

Realistic stories are ones that have characters and events that *seem* so real that they might really have happened. But you don't know for sure if they really *did* happen. Now look at the contents and choose a selection that is a realistic story.

Informational articles give you facts or information. Sometimes informational articles tell you how to make or do something. They sometimes tell you facts about different countries. Sometimes they tell you a lot about one thing, such as an article about dinosaurs of long ago. Informational articles also tell you about history, or things that really happened in the past. Now, choose an informational article from the contents.

The following paragraphs tell about people who are reading stories and informational selections. Read each paragraph and decide whether they are reading a realistic story or an informational article.

Wallace is reading about the American astronauts who landed on the moon on July 20, 1969. They were the first men to ever set foot on the moon. What type of selection is Wallace reading?

Rhoda is reading about three children who went down to the stream to fish. All three of the children brought their new fishing poles along. They were each hoping to catch the biggest fish that day. All three children baited their hooks and cast their lines. What type of selection is Rhoda reading?

Lorene is reading about famous baseball players. She is learning that Hank Aaron broke the home run record set by Babe Ruth. What type of selection is Lorene reading?

In the future, as you read many different kinds of selections, see if you can pick out those that are either realistic stories or informational articles.

By Sandy Shores

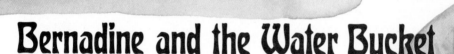

Bernadine and the Water Bucket

by Aileen Olsen

Bernadine lives on an island, an island surrounded by warm blue sea. The island is not very big. If you were grown up, you could walk all the way across it between sunrise and sunset.

Bernadine lives in a house close to the sea, with her mother, her father and a goat named Alice. Behind the house are the sugar cane fields where Bernadine's father works. Sometimes, for a treat, Bernadine's father brings her a piece of sugar cane to chew. The stalk of the sugar cane is sweet and juicy.

Every day, Bernadine's mother walks to the village to get water for drinking and cooking from the village water pipe. Bernadine loves to go with her mother to the village. They carry water buckets on their heads. Bernadine carries a small bucket. Her mother carries a big one. Someday, her mother says, Bernadine can go alone to the village to get water. Bernadine is waiting . . . what a wonderful, grown-up thing to do!

This morning Bernadine's mother is weeding the sweet potato patch. She calls to Bernadine, "I am so busy that I do not have time to go to the village for water. Do you think you could go alone, little one?"

"Yes, yes," says Bernadine. "I can go alone, Mama." Bernadine is so excited that she nearly falls out of the breadfruit tree where she has been sitting watching the schooner *Rosemary* sail into the bay.

"Well then," her mother says, "take the small bucket and do not fill it full. Leave some room so the water will not splash out. And be back by lunchtime. Papa will want tea with his lunch."

So Bernadine takes the small bucket. And something else. She takes along the coconut shell sailboat that her father made for her.

"I don't think you can manage the bucket and the coconut boat too, Bernadine," her mother says.

"Yes, I can. See?" Bernadine lifts the empty bucket onto her head with one hand while she holds the boat with the other hand.

Her mother looks doubtful for a moment. Then she smiles. "All right. Go along. I know you are getting to be a big girl."

With a laugh and a good-bye wave, Bernadine runs down the beach toward the village.

The beach is also the road to the village. People, and animals, too, walk along the beach. Here comes a friend, Mr. Hamilton-Brown, and his donkey. They are bringing home a big stalk of young green bananas. "Good morning, Mr. Hamilton-Brown," says Bernadine. "I am going alone to the village to get water."

"Alone? Ah, that is fine. Luck be with you."

Bernadine walks beneath tall coconut palms and in and out of the shallow water. How soft it feels. It would be lovely to swim . . . but she is going to the village to get water.

Who comes now? It is the Grandmother of
Janette and John Peter, Bernadine's good friends.
Today, Grandmother is carrying a basket of
oranges on her head. She is leading a fat pink pig
she has bought at the market in the village.

"Good morning, Bernadine. Do you like my pig?"

"Yes, he is lovely. But I must hurry. I am going to
the village alone to get water."

"Ha, good luck to you then, little one."

At last, Bernadine reaches the village. By now the

warm sun has climbed above the green mountain in the middle of the island. There are many people going to the market and many are filling their buckets at the water pipe.

"You came alone?" says one.

"Without your mother?" says another. They are all surprised.

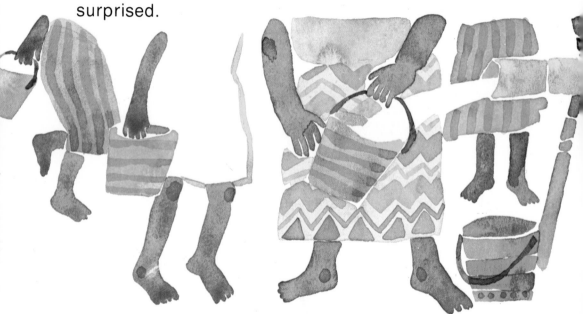

Bernadine waits for her turn at the water pipe. Then she fills her bucket—not quite full—just as her mother told her. But with the water in it, the bucket is heavy. Bernadine must use both hands to lift the bucket onto her head. And what about her coconut boat, lying on the stones? How can she pick it up without spilling the water? Oh, dear!

"Here, Bernadine, I hand you your boat." A man from the village helps her.

Bernadine is proud and happy. The bucket of water is safely on her head, balanced with one hand, and she has her coconut boat.

"Good luck to you, little one," the people of the village call to her as she walks back down the beach.

Now the sun is straight above her head and it is very warm. Who is coming? It is her good friends, Janette and John Peter.

"Good morning, Bernadine. Where are you going?"

"Good morning, Janette. Good morning, John Peter. I have been to the village alone to get water."

"We are going for a swim," says John Peter.

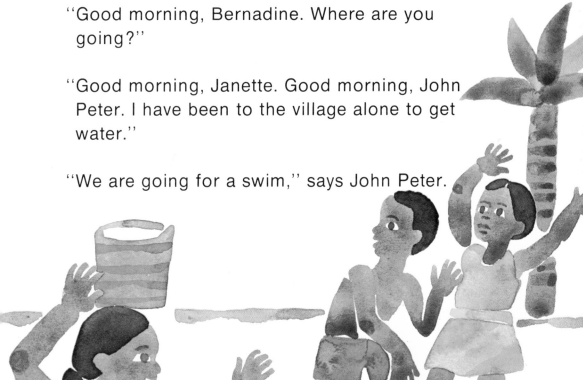

"Yes, come with us," says Janette.

Bernadine is very warm and the sea begs her with its blue wetness. Should she? Well . . . just a little swim. She will still be home with the water in time for lunch. Bernadine puts her bucket down in the shade of a coconut palm. Then the three friends run splashing into the sea.

"John Peter, watch. I sail my boat." Bernadine sets the coconut boat on a wave and the wind pushes the tiny white sail. The boat rides up, down. John Peter and Janette each have a turn at sailing the coconut boat. Up, down. Blue sea, carry me.

Bernadine likes to float on her stomach and look through the clear water at the bright fishes. There are yellow and black striped ones, red ones with waving fins, and tiny silvery ones. They tickle her arms and legs as they swim close to her.

There are sea urchins too, black and bristly, on the bottom. The children are careful not to step on them for they are very sharp. But what is this? A pink conch shell half-buried in the sand.

Bernadine saves shells for the border of the path that leads from her house to the beach. This shell is especially pretty. Bernadine dives down and picks it up.

"See what I have found," she calls to her friends.

"Oh, but how shall I carry it home?"

"In the bucket," says John Peter. "The shell is clean. It has been washed by the sea for a long, long time."

"Yes. But come and help me. I must hurry, for it is almost lunchtime and Papa needs water for his tea."

Janette and John Peter run to get Bernadine's bucket.

"Look, you have a passenger," says Janette. A tiny baby lizard has fallen from the palm tree and is riding on a bit of palm leaf in Bernadine's bucket.

"Oooooh, look at him now," says Bernadine. "He is lovely. I will take him home to live in our breadfruit tree."

Carefully, Bernadine drops the conch shell into the water, under the lizard. Then she lifts the bucket onto her head and John Peter hands her the coconut boat.

"Good-bye, good-bye." Janette and John Peter go up the path to their house on the side of the mountain.

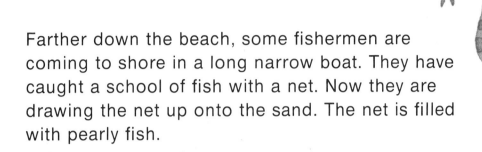

Farther down the beach, some fishermen are coming to shore in a long narrow boat. They have caught a school of fish with a net. Now they are drawing the net up onto the sand. The net is filled with pearly fish.

Bernadine must stop to watch. Everyone who lives nearby is coming to see if the fishermen have a good catch. The fishermen always give some fish to their friends. A pushing, laughing crowd of people are wading into the water to get their fish. Bernadine would love to have a fish to take home to Mama—a fine fish to fry for lunch. But how could she possibly carry the bucket with the lizard and the shell in it . . . and the coconut boat . . . and the fish, too?

One of the fishermen sees Bernadine. "Here, little one. Here is a fish for you," he calls, and throws a fat fish that lands in the sand at Bernadine's feet.

Now what can she do? The fish is big and slippery to carry. Should she leave the coconut boat behind? No, her little boat with its mast and sail was a gift from her father. Should she leave the bucket behind? No, her mother needs the water for Papa's tea.

At last Bernadine decides. She takes the fish into the sea and washes it until there is not a grain of sand on its pearly scales. Now it is as shiny and clean as the shell that came from the sea. Then, carefully, she slides the fish into the bucket, under the leaf where the lizard sits. The fish is so big that the water spills over the top of the bucket. To make room for the fish and the shell and the lizard, Bernadine must tip a little more water out of the bucket.

But what about the coconut boat, lying on the sand? The fishermen have gone away and there is no one to hand it to her. It, too, must go into the bucket. So Bernadine takes the boat into the sea and washes it as carefully as she washed the fish. Then she tips out a little more water. Now there is just enough room in the bucket for the boat to ride on the water beside the lizard. She puts the bucket on her head again and goes down the beach, walking tall and straight. Hurry, it is late!

At home, Papa is just coming from the cane field. Mama is waiting by the cooking stove outside the house.

"See what I bring," calls Bernadine.

'Indeed, water I hope," her mother says.

'Bernadine has been to the village alone to get water," her mother tells her father.

Bernadine sets the bucket on the ground. Mama looks into the bucket. For a moment she says nothing. Then she laughs. "Bernadine has carried some things besides the water." She holds up the coconut boat and the lizard for Papa to see. She looks again into the bucket. What is this? She pulls the fat pearly fish and the pink conch shell out of the water.

Now Bernadine's mother and father are both laughing. "Ha, Bernadine," her father says, "I did not know there are fish and shells in the water pipe at the village."

Bernadine laughs, too.

"That is not such good water for tea any more," her mother says.

"I have an idea," Papa says. "Alice needs water to drink. The goat will not mind that the fish and the shell and the boat and the lizard have all been in the water. We can give Alice the water, and I will milk Alice. We will have goat's milk for lunch instead of tea."

Bernardine's father milks Alice while her mother fries the fish. Bernadine puts the baby lizard on the trunk of the breadfruit tree. He jumps onto a glossy green leaf, very much at home. And the beautiful shell is put on the path, right beside the step leading into Bernadine's house.

Alice gulps down every drop of the water from

Bernadine's bucket. And Bernadine, her mother and her father all have a delicious lunch of fried fish and sweet potatoes and goat's milk. Oh yes, and a piece of juicy sugar cane to chew for dessert.

Talking It Over

1. Why did Bernadine bring home more than just water?

2. How do you think Bernadine's parents felt about the things she brought home? Why do you think as you do?

Fun with Sand

by Bernice Kohn

What do you think of when someone says "beach"? If you are like many people, you think of sand. Sand—because on most beaches there's so much of it. You can walk on it, roll in it, dig in it, and sleep on it. It gets between your toes, in your ears, in your hair—and, too often, even in your mouth.

Just because sand is so plentiful, you probably don't pay much attention to it. If you stop to think about it, sand is more interesting than it looks. Sand is really rock that has been ground down by the action of water. The kind of sand on a particular beach depends on the kind of rock on that shore. Different kinds of rock make different colors of sand. The most common color of sand in the United States is gray, but there is also white sand in Florida and New Mexico, and green sand in Hawaii. In other countries you can find beaches that are red, black, or pink.

No matter what color the sand is, most people don't take it home (except in their shoes). But if you are willing to take home a bagful, you can make sand paintings. The directions that follow will tell you how.

How to Make a Sand Painting

You will need:

a pail or coffee can of sand

liquid food coloring

several jars with tops

newspapers or paper towels

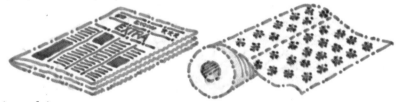

sheets of heavy paper or cardboard

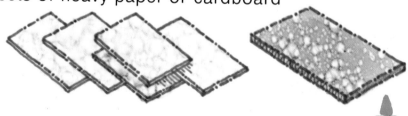

white glue in a squeeze bottle

plastic wrap for covering your painting

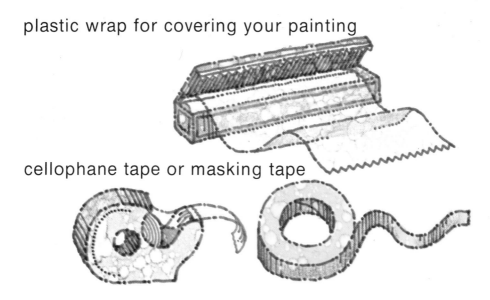

cellophane tape or masking tape

You will probably want to use several different colors of sand to make your sand painting. If all the sand in your area is one color, you will have to color your sand before you make the painting. Here's how to do it.

To color the sand:

1. Decide what colors you want to use. Then pick one jar for each color. Put a small amount of sand into each jar.

2. Add a few drops of liquid food coloring to the sand. The more food coloring you add, the darker the color of the sand will become.

3. Cover the jar and shake it well.

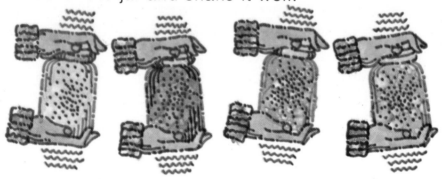

4. Spread the colored sand from each jar on a newspaper or paper towel to dry. Let it stand overnight.

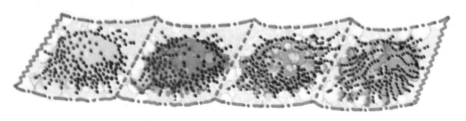

To make the painting:

1. Plan a design or picture. You might like to draw it lightly in pencil on your paper or cardboard. Keep it simple. Try not to draw many small details.

2. Spread glue over a small section of your design.

3. Sprinkle colored sand over the wet glue. Do one color at a time. Shake off the extra sand before you use another color.

4. Continue spreading glue and sprinkling sand on small sections until your painting is finished.

5. Let the glue dry. Shake off any loose sand. There may be some bare patches here and there. Fill them in with a drop of glue and add sand.

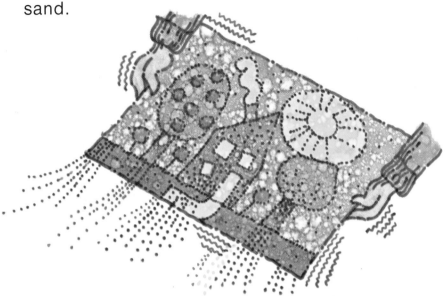

6. Let the painting dry. To protect your picture, cover it with clear plastic wrap. Fold the ends of the wrap behind the painting. Tape the wrap to the back of the picture.

Books to Enjoy

Fish Is Fish
by Leo Lionni
A fish and a tadpole grow up in a pond together. When the tadpole becomes a frog, he leaves the pond. But he comes back and tells the fish about what he has seen in the world. You'll want to find out what happens when the fish tries to see the world too.

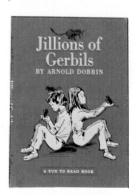

Jillions of Gerbils
by Arnold Dobrin
Just after David and Rosie move into a big old house, David's pet gerbil disappears. When he gets another gerbil, it too disappears. Then the children find a secret door that leads to a big surprise. Read this book to see what the surprise is!

Josephine's 'magination
by Arnold Dobrin
When Josephine and her mother go to the market, Josephine never has enough money to buy what she really wants. But one day she learns about *'magination.* If you read this book you'll find out how Josephine's 'magination helps her get what she really wants.

Book jacket reprinted by permission of Four Winds Press, a division of Scholastic Magazines, Inc., from *Josephine's 'Magination,* © 1973 by Arnold Dobrin.

Maria's House
by Jean Merrill

Maria thinks that art should be beautiful. But her art teacher has asked her to draw a picture of her own house. Maria's house! An ugly, run-down apartment building! Read the book and find out what Maria decides to do.

Dance, Dance, Amy-Chan!
by Lucy Hawkinson

Amy wants so much to dance in the street festival. She practices the butterfly dance for weeks. But Amy's little sister always hangs around. Susie's too little to dance, but not too little to stir up trouble! Read the story to see what Susie does and how Amy handles it.

When the Whale Came to My Town
by Jim Young

This is the true story of a boy who finds a whale lying on the beach. He spends three days with the whale, watching the Coast Guard trying to help it. The boy never forgets his experience, and you'll find his story hard to forget too.

Glossary

Full Pronunciation Key

The pronunciation of each word is shown just after the word, in this way: **ab bre vi ate** (ə brē/vē āt). The letters and signs used are pronounced as in the words below. The mark / is placed after a syllable with primary or heavy accent, as in the example above. The mark / after a syllable shows a secondary or lighter accent, as in **ab bre vi a tion** (ə brē/vē ā/shən).

a	hat, cap	j	jam, enjoy	u	cup, butter
ā	age, face	k	kind, seek	ù	full, put
ä	father, far	l	land, coal	ü	rule, move
		m	me, am		
		n	no, in		
b	bad, rob	ng	long, bring		
ch	child, much			v	very, save
d	did, red			w	will, woman
		o	hot, rock	y	young, yet
		ō	open, go	z	zero, breeze
e	let, best	ô	order, all	zh	measure, seizure
ē	equal, be	oi	oil, voice		
ėr	term, learn	ou	house, out		
f	fat, if	p	paper, cup	ə	represents:
g	go, bag	r	run, try		a in about
h	he, how	s	say, yes		e in taken
		sh	she, rush		i in pencil
		t	tell, it		o in lemon
i	it, pin	th	thin, both		u in circus
ī	ice, five	ŦH	then, smooth		

This pronunciation key is from the *Thorndike-Barnhart Beginning Dictionary,* Eighth Edition, Copyright © 1974 by Scott, Foresman and Company. The definitions in this glossary are adapted from the *Thorndike-Barnhart Beginning Dictionary.*

an noy (ə noi′), make somewhat angry; disturb: *The long drive always annoys my father.* verb.

anx ious (angk′shəs), **1** uneasy because of thoughts or fears about what may happen; troubled; worried: *Mother felt anxious about the children, who had been gone an hour too long.* **2** wishing very much; eager: *She was anxious to please her mother.* adjective.

a pol o get ic (ə pol′ə jet′ik), making an excuse; expressing regret: *He sent me an apologetic note saying he was sorry for forgetting to come to my party.* adjective.

Ar i zo na (ar′ə zō′nə), state in the SW United States. noun.

bar na cle (bär′nə kəl), small salt water animal with a shell that attaches itself to rocks, the bottoms of ships, the timber of wharves, etc. See the picture. noun.

Ber na dine (bèr′nə dēn′). noun.

blade (blād), **1** the cutting part of anything like a knife or sword: *My mother's carving knife has a very sharp blade.* **2** a leaf of grass. **3** the flat, wide part of anything. The propeller of an airplane or helicopter has blades. noun.

blush (blush), become red in the face because of shame, confusion, or excitement: *The little boy was so shy that he blushed every time he was spoken to.* verb.

boast (bōst), speak too highly of oneself or what one owns: *He boasts about his grades in school.* verb.

bris tle (bris′əl), one of the short, stiff hairs of some animals or plants: *Brushes are often made of the bristles of hogs.* noun.

bris tly (bris′lē), **1** rough with bristles or hair like bristles: *The trapper had a bristly chin after a week in the woods.* **2** like bristles: *bristly hair.* adjective, **bris tli er, bris tli est.**

British Columbia, province in SW Canada, on the Pacific Ocean. *Capital:* Victoria.

hat, āge, fär;
let, ēqual, tèrm; it, īce;
hot, ōpen, ôrder;
oil, out;
cup, pùt, rüle;
ch, child; ng, long;
sh, she;
th, thin; ᴛʜ, then;
zh, measure;

ə represents *a* in about,
e in taken, *i* in pencil,
o in lemon, *u* in circus.

barnacle

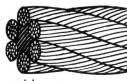

cable

cab in (kab/ən), **1** a small, roughly built house. **2** a private room in a ship. **3** place for passengers in an aircraft. *noun.*

ca ble (kā/bəl), a strong, thick rope, usually made of wires twisted together. See the picture. *noun.*

Can a da (kan/ə də), the country north of the United States. *noun.*

cel lo phane (sel/ə fān), transparent substance somewhat like paper. It is used as a wrapping to keep food or candy fresh and clean. *noun.*

cer e mo ni al (ser/ə mō/nē əl), of or having something to do with ceremony. *adjective.*

cer e mo ny (ser/ə mō/nē), a special act or set of acts to be done on special occasions such as weddings, funerals, graduations, or holidays. *noun, plural* **cer e mo nies.**

Chey enne (shī an/ *or* shī en/ *for 1;* shī en/ *for 2,3*), **1** capital of Wyoming. **2** member of an Algonquian tribe of Indians, now living in Montana and Oklahoma. **3** their language. *noun, plural* **Chey enne** *or* **Chey ennes** *for 2.*

cir cuit (sėr/kit), **1** a going around; a moving around: *The earth takes a year to make its circuit of the sun.* **2** the complete path or a part of it over which an electric current flows. *noun.*

com put er (kəm pyü/tər), machine which computes, especially an electronic machine that solves complex mathematical problems in a very short time when given certain information. *noun.*

con tra dict (kon/trə dikt/), **1** say that a statement is not true; deny. **2** say the opposite of what a person has said. *verb.*

con trol (kən trōl/), **1** have power or authority over; direct: *A captain controls the ship and its crew.* **2** device that controls a machine: *The control of our furnace can be operated from the kitchen.* **3 the controls,** the instruments and devices by which an airplane, locomotive, or car is operated: *The new pilot managed the controls better in taking off than in landing.* **1** *verb,* **con trolled, con trol ling.** **2,3** *noun.*

de tail (di tāl′ *or* dē′tāl), small or unimportant part: *All the details of her costume carried out the brown color scheme. noun.*

down y (dou′nē), of soft feathers, hair, or fluff: *a downy pillow. adjective,* **down i er, down i est.**

em bar rass (em bar′əs), make uneasy and ashamed; make self-conscious: *He was embarrassed when he spilled his bowl of soup. verb.*

em broi der y (em broi′dər ē), ornamental designs sewn in cloth or leather with a needle. *noun, plural* **em broi der ies.**

en gi neer (en′jə nir′), **1** person who takes care of or runs engines. **2** person who plans and builds engines, machines, roads, bridges, canals, forts, and the like. *noun.*

e nor mous (i nôr′məs), very, very large; huge. *adjective.*

es cort (es′kôrt *for 1 and 2,* e skôrt′ *for 3*), **1** one or more persons going with other persons, or with valuable goods, to see that they keep safe, or to honor them: *An escort of ten police officers accompanied the famous visitor.* **2** one or more ships or airplanes serving as a guard. **3** go with to keep safe or to honor: *Warships escorted the steamer.* **1,2** *noun,* **3** *verb.*

ex as pe rate (eg zas′pə rāt′), irritate very much; annoy greatly; make angry: *The children's noise exasperated their parents. verb,* **ex as pe rat ed, ex as pe rat ing.**

ex pe di tion (ek′spə dish′ən), **1** journey for a special purpose, such as war, discovery, or collecting new plants. **2** the people or ships that make such a journey. *noun.*

fes tiv i ty (fe stiv′ə tē), a rejoicing and feasting; merry party: *The wedding festivities were very happy. noun, plural* **fes tiv i ties.**

fierce (firs), **1** savage; wild: *A wounded lion can be fierce.* **2** raging; violent: *fierce anger. A fierce wind blows very hard. adjective,* **fierc er, fierc est.**

hat, āge, fär;
let, ēqual, tėrm; it, īce;
hot, ōpen, ôrder;
oil, out;
cup, pút, rüle;
ch, child; ng, long;
sh, she;
th, thin; ŦH, then;
zh, measure;

ə represents *a* in about,
e in taken, *i* in pencil,
o in lemon, *u* in circus.

funnel
(definition 1)

funnel
(definition 2)
funnels on a
steamship

helicopter

fun nel (fun′l), **1** a tapering tube with a wide mouth shaped like a cone. See the picture. **2** smokestack or chimney on a steamship or steam engine. See the picture. *noun.*

gen er ous (jen′ər əs), **1** willing to share with others; unselfish. **2** noble and forgiving; not mean. *adjective.*

gloom (glüm), **1** darkness; deep shadow; dim light. **2** dark thoughts and feelings; low spirits; sadness. *noun.*

grad u ate (graj′ü āt), finish the course of a school or college and be given a diploma or paper saying so. *verb,* **grad u at ed, grad u at ing.**

grad u a tion (graj′ü ā′shən), **1** a graduating from a school or college. **2** ceremony of graduating; graduating exercises. *noun.*

har bor (här′bər), place of shelter for ships. *noun.*

hel i cop ter (hel′ə kop′tər), aircraft that is lifted from the ground and kept in the air by horizontal rotor blades. See the picture. *noun.*

Ho pi (hō′pē), **1** member of a tribe of Pueblo Indians living in adobe-built villages in northern Arizona. **2** their language. *noun, plural* **Ho pis** for 1.

im pa tient (im pā′shənt), **1** not patient; not willing to bear delay, opposition, pain, or bother: *He is impatient with his little brother.* **2** uneasy and eager; restless: *The horses were impatient to start in the race.* **3** showing lack of patience: *an impatient answer. adjective.*

inch (inch), **1** a measure of length, 1/12 of a foot. **2** move slowly or little by little: *The worm inched along.* 1 *noun, plural* **inch es;** 2 *verb.*

in stru ment (in′strə mənt), thing used to do something; tool; mechanical device. *noun.*

in vent (in vent′), make or think out (something new): *Alexander Graham Bell invented the telephone. verb.*

in ven tion (in ven′shən), **1** making something new: *the invention of the clock.* **2** the thing invented: *Television is a modern invention. noun.*

in ven tor (in ven′tər), person who invents: *Banneker was an early inventor. noun.*

in ves ti gate (in ves′tə gāt), search into; examine closely: *Detectives investigate crimes to find out who did them. Scientists investigate nature to learn more about it. verb,* **in ves ti gat ed, in ves ti gat ing.**

jel ly fish (jel′ē fish′), a sea animal like a lump of jelly. See the picture. *noun, plural* **jel ly fish es** or **jel ly fish.**

jet engine, an engine driven by a jet of air or gas. See the diagram.

kneel (nēl), go down on one's knee or knees: *I kneel to weed the garden. He knelt down to pull a weed from the flower bed. verb,* **knelt** or **kneeled, kneel ing.**

knelt (nelt). See **kneel.** *He knelt to pick up the pieces. verb.*

launch (lônch), **1** cause to slide into the water; set afloat: *The new ship was launched from the supports on which it was built.* **2** act of launching a rocket, missile, aircraft, or ship: *The launch of the first space vehicle was a historic event.* **1** *verb,* **2** *noun, plural* **launch es.**

liq uid (lik′wid), **1** any substance that is not a solid or a gas; substance that flows freely like water. **2** in the form of a liquid; melted: *liquid soap, butter heated until it is liquid.* **1** *noun,* **2** *adjective.*

Lo ma hong va (lō mä′hong vä′). *noun.*

mast (mast), long pole of wood or steel set upright on a ship to support the sails and rigging. See the picture. *noun.*

mast

hat, āge, fär;
let, ēqual, tėrm; it, īce;
hot, ōpen, ôrder;
oil, out;
cup, put, rüle;
ch, child; ng, long;
sh, she;
th, thin; ₮H, then;
zh, measure;

ə represents *a* in about,
e in taken, *i* in pencil,
o in lemon, *u* in circus.

jellyfish

AIR COMPRESSOR   FUEL SPRAY   TURBINE

AIR   SHAFT   BURNER   JET EXHAUST

jet engine
The air is sucked in through the front of the engine, compressed, and mixed with fuel. This mixture is burned in the burners, giving off gas that passes out in a powerful jet through the rear of the engine, pushing the airplane forward.

MAST

SAILS

mast

octopus
(from 6 inches to
20 feet across,
depending on the
species)

palm¹

palm²

Milky Way, a broad band of faint light that stretches across the sky at night. It is made up of countless stars, too far away to be seen separately without a telescope.

Na nai mo (nə nī′mō). *noun.*

oc to pus (ok′tə pəs), a sea animal having a soft, stout body and eight arms with suckers on them. See the picture. *noun, plural* **oc to pus es, oc to pi.**

O-kom (ō′kom). *noun.*

palm¹ (päm), the inside of the hand between the wrist and the fingers. See the picture. *noun.*

palm² (päm), any of many kinds of trees growing in warm climates. Most palms have tall trunks, no branches, and many large leaves at the top. See the picture. *noun.*

pas sen ger (pas′ən jər), traveler in a train, bus, boat, etc., usually one that pays a fare. *noun.*

pa tience (pā′shəns), calm bearing of pain, of waiting, or of anything that annoys, troubles, or hurts: *The cat showed patience by watching the mouse hole. noun.*

pa tient (pā′shənt), having patience; showing patience. *adjective.*

pearl y (pėr′lē), like a pearl in color or luster: *pearly teeth. adjective,* **pearl i er, pearl i est.**

pi lot (pī′lət), **1** person who steers a ship or boat. **2** person who operates the controls of an aircraft in flight. **3** act as a pilot of; steer: *The aviator pilots the airplane.* **1,2** *noun,* **3** *verb.*

port hole (pôrt′hōl′), opening in a ship's side to let in light and air. *noun.*

prair ie (prer′ē), a large area of level or rolling land with grass but few or no trees. *noun.*

pro gram (prō′gram), **1** items making up an entertainment: *The entire program was delightful.* **2** set of instructions for an electronic computer outlining the steps to be performed by the machine in a specific operation. *noun.*

pro test (prō′test *for 1;* prə test′ *for 2*),
1 statement that denies or objects strongly:
They yielded only after protest. **2** make
objections; object: *The children protested
against having grown-ups in the game.*
1 *noun,* 2 *verb.*

quite (kwīt), **1** completely; entirely: *a hat quite
out of fashion. I am quite alone.* **2** really; truly:
quite a change in the weather. **3** very; rather;
somewhat: *It is quite hot. adverb.*

reign (rān), **1** period of power of a ruler: *The
queen's reign lasted fifty years.* **2** rule: *A king
reigns over his kingdom.* 1 *noun,* 2 *verb.*

re luc tant (ri luk′tənt), unwilling; slow to act
because unwilling: *I am reluctant to go out in
very cold weather. adjective.*

rig ging (rig′ing), rope, chains, and cables used
to support and work the masts, yards, and sails
on a ship. *noun.*

ro tor (rō′tər), **1** the rotating part of a machine or
apparatus. **2** system of rotating blades by
which a helicopter is enabled to fly. See the
picture under **helicopter.** *noun.*

school[1] (skül), place for teaching and learning:
Children go to school to learn. noun.

school[2] (skül), large number of the same kind of
fish or water animals swimming together: *a
school of mackerel. noun.*

scut tle[1] (skut′l), a kind of bucket for holding or
carrying coal. See the picture. *noun.*

scut tle[2] (skut′l), scamper; scurry: *The dogs
scuttled off into the woods.* **scut tled,
scut tling.** *verb.*

sea coast (sē′kōst′), land along the sea: *the
seacoast of North America. noun.*

sea urchin, any of a group of small, round sea
animals with spiny shells. See the picture.

sea weed (sē′wēd′), any plant or plants growing
in the sea. *noun.*

hat, āge, fär;
let, ēqual, tėrm; it, īce;
hot, ōpen, ôrder;
oil, out;
cup, pùt, rüle;
ch, child; ng, long;
sh, she;
th, thin; ŦH, then;
zh, measure;

ə represents *a* in about,
e in taken, *i* in pencil,
o in lemon, *u* in circus.

scuttle[1]

sea urchin
(diameter
about 3 inches)

totem
definition 2)
Indian totem pole

shel ter (shel′tər), **1** something that covers or protects from weather, danger, or attack: *Trees are a shelter from the sun.* **2** protection; refuge: *We took shelter from the storm in a barn. noun.*

stern[1] (stėrn), severe; strict; harsh: *His stern frown frightened the people. adjective.*

stern[2] (stėrn), the hind part of a ship or boat. *noun.*

switch (swich), **1** a slender stick used in whipping. **2** device for making or breaking a connection in an electric circuit. **3** change or shift: *switch places.* **1,2** *noun, plural* **switch es;** **3** *verb.*

to tem (tō′təm), **1** a natural object, often an animal, taken as the emblem of a tribe, clan, or family. **2** image of such an object. Totems are often carved and painted on poles. See the picture. *noun.*

Ty ee (tī ē′). *noun.*

ur gent (ėr′jənt), demanding immediate action or attention: *an urgent duty; an urgent message. adjective.*

vague (vāg), not definite; not clear; not distinct: *In a fog everything looks vague. adjective,* **va guer, va guest.**

Van cou ver (van kü′vər), a seaport city in southwestern Canada. *noun.*

vet er i nar i an (vet′ər ə ner′ē ən), doctor or surgeon who treats animals. *noun.*

war y (wer′ē *or* war′ē), on one's guard against danger or deception: *a wary fox. adjective,* **war i er, war i est.**

3 4 5 6 7 8 9 10 11 12 13 14 15 16 17 18 19 20 21 22 23 24 25 RRD 82 81 80 79 78 77